David Hockney
The East Yorkshire Landscape

David Hockney
The East Yorkshire Landscape

9 February – 24 March 2007

L | A | LOUVER

FOREWORD

In February and March of this year, L.A. Louver presented an exhibition of new works by David Hockney, entitled *The East Yorkshire Landscape*. This extraordinary group of paintings followed on from a show of David's watercolors,[1] presented in the gallery during 2005. At that time, this exhibition represented the high point of David's achievement with the medium with which he had worked exclusively for the preceding three years. Armed with all of the new knowledge he had acquired from having worked so directly on paper with translucent watercolors, David returned to Los Angeles to prepare for that beautiful exhibition, and to paint with oil on canvas. From this visit a series of portraits of friends emerged, which we in turn had an opportunity to experience in the retrospective exhibition of portraits that traveled from Boston, to Los Angeles, and ultimately to London in 2006 – 2007.[2] Of course, as on many occasions during David's career, making portraits has been a way for the artist to return to the canvas. At this time David's ambition was focused on capturing his response to the East Yorkshire landscape as a subject, and in images centered on his feelings for the place, time and memory from this space of his youth.

Fortunately for us in Southern California, Stephanie Barron, the Senior Curator of Modern Art at the Los Angeles County Museum of Art, visited David Hockney in his Yorkshire studio during the late summer of 2006. Stephanie was amazed by what the artist had already produced: plein air landscape paintings on canvas, made quickly and boldly with big brushes involving a vivid palette, often on multiple canvases, which were taken out in the four-wheel drive vehicle down country lanes, into the open fields. During this visit, Stephanie reminded David that the great touring exhibition of John Constable's studio landscape paintings,[3] together with his controversial attendant six-foot sketches of the same subjects, would soon be traveling to its last venue at the Huntington in San Marino, California. Stephanie suggested to David that an audience should have the opportunity to experience two English painters, concerned in their respective times with innovative ways of considering landscape painting. Soon David was on the phone, and the idea of *The East Yorkshire Landscape* exhibition was born.

Given the spontaneity of this decision and the urgency with which David was pursuing his new motifs, we decided to publish the accompanying exhibition catalogue at a later date. This timing enabled David to utilize every available minute to work with his chosen landscape subject, through the changing seasons, and to be able to respond, in real time, to feelings evoked from the diminishing duration of daylight, seasonal changing foliage, and nature's definition of space. This decision also meant that we could leave our selection of the paintings to be exhibited to the very last minute available, and for David to plan precisely how these works could be uniquely installed in the gallery. As such, in this catalogue we made a selection of installation photographs to memorialize the experience of the show. A short film[4] was also made for L.A. Louver. This, together with a complete account of the exhibition, can be viewed on our Web site[5].

Five of the paintings entitled *Woldgate Woods* were selected from an ongoing, as yet to be completed series of paintings of the four seasons. Following a visit to the Constable exhibition in San Marino and to David's Los Angeles studio by Stephen Deuchar, Director of Tate Britain, it was decided that this same group of paintings would also be shown at the Tate. From the summer of 2007 until February 2008, these five *Woldgate Woods* paintings can be seen at Tate Britain,[6] to coincide with an exhibition of J.M.W. Turner's watercolors, selected by David Hockney from the museum's significant holdings.[7]

While David Hockney was in Los Angeles for *The East Yorkshire Landscape* exhibition, he began to ponder how far this idea of multiple-canvas "combine" paintings could be extended. David also reflected upon the process he developed in making the first of his multiple canvas paintings, entitled *A Closer Winter Tunnel, February – March, 2006,*[8] which led to the *Woldgate Woods* series. For this painting, David employed a digital photographic reproduction technique that allowed him to study, as the work evolved, the assembled image of the painting in the studio prior to each new day's work in the landscape. He even made marks directly onto each paper collage, thereby providing himself with a fresh starting point for that morning's painting activity.

With these thoughts in mind, while standing in the gallery in front of his painting entitled *Tree Off The Track,* in which all of the canvases are joined together; having just visited Paris to view the reinstallation of Monet's waterlily paintings;[9] and at the same time considering other possible Yorkshire landscape motifs, David resolved and began planning technically how to undertake making a 50-canvas painting [each panel 36 x 48 in. (91.4 x 121.9 cm)] of a certain grove of trees beside a farmhouse in the East Yorkshire landscape. He considered how to visualize the progress of the painting of this collective image while working on each individual small canvas, in situ. David then realized that by extending the experience he had learned from making earlier multiple canvas paintings, he could form in the studio, after each day's work in the fields, an elaborate digital photographic paper collage mosaic and, thereby as the work progressed, maintain a clear perspective of the painting as a whole. This work, now complete, will be shown in this summer's Royal Academy exhibition.[10] *Bigger Trees Near Warter* is an oil painting which could not have been made without the aid of a computer, and by utilizing both "high and low" technology.[11]

As I think back to David Hockney's response to photography, from his collages of the Grand Canyon, to the large photographic wall mural[12] resulting from his response to the husbandry of the open East Yorkshire landscape; from the plains of York with its 60-mile horizon, to Garrowby Hill,[13] and the spaces formed due to the changing surface of the chalk hills in these little valleys of agricultural wolds[14] (with which David had long made an association to the American West), I also find a connection to his current ambition.[15] Continually, David has responded to what he has often referred to as "the tyranny of vanishing-point perspective," and to his ongoing study of image making. From these considerations, together with those of the paintings of Caravaggio, Brunelleschi's Baptistry, optical projections, mirrors, Vermeer, the camera image, and questions concerning how the lens has contributed,

via the media, to affect our view of the world, we are led to his book entitled, *Secret Knowledge.*[16] From there, David Hockney takes us on this unbelievable journey to this moment in time and to his actions as a painter.

This catalogue is being published in July 2007 on the occasion of David Hockney's 70th birthday, in celebration of our exhibition and his life as an artist working at the top of his game. The other paintings illustrated in this book and which formed a major part of the exhibition are now in private collections in Los Angeles, Pasadena, San Francisco and the Bay Area, Seattle, Boston, Pennsylvania, and Sydney, Australia — many ultimately destined for donation to public collections.

Many thanks are due; to Stephanie Barron at LACMA, who has been a good friend and colleague for more than 30 years; to John Murdoch, Director of Art Collections at the Huntington, who so graciously and enthusiastically embraced the Constable-Hockney axiom; to the indomitable studio assistant Jean-Pierre Goncalves, who works with David in the fields, and whose photography gives us another view into the artist's working process; to Gregory Evans, David's personal assistant with whom it is an ongoing pleasure to collaborate; to all of the studio staff, especially

Richard Schmidt, and their technology consultant
Erik Arnesen, Karen Kuhlman, Julie Pavlowski
and Greg Rose; and of course, to all of my extraordinary
colleagues at L.A. Louver, especially to my personal
assistant Lisa Jann, co-directors Kimberly Davis and
Elizabeth East, and our Chief Preparator Chris Pate,
who engineered this very special installation; and to our
catalogue designer Stefan Bucher.

My very special thanks to David Hockney
for entrusting me for all these years with his work,
and these paintings in particular.

Happy Birthday, David. I cannot wait for tomorrow,
and more of your ideas. As you are often heard
to say to others: Love Life.

Peter Goulds

Sunday, 6 May 2007
Topanga Canyon, California

1   *Hand Eye Heart: Watercolors of the East Yorkshire Landscape,*
    L.A. Louver, Venice, California, 26 February – 2 April 2005.

2   *Hockney Portraits,* Museum of Fine Arts, Boston, MA,
    26 February – 14 May 2006; traveled to Los Angeles County
    Museum of Art, Los Angeles, California, 11 June –
    4 September 2006; and National Portrait Gallery, London,
    England, 12 October 2006 – 21 January 2007.

3   *Constable: The Great Landscapes,* Tate Britain, London, England,
    1 June – 28 August 2006; *Constable's Great Landscapes:*
    The Six-Foot Paintings, National Gallery of Art, Washington, D.C.,
    1 October 2006 – 2 January 2007; traveled to the Huntington,
    San Marino, California, 3 February – 29 April 2007.

4   A short video of the installation of *The East Yorkshire Landscape*
    at L.A. Louver was produced and directed by Hannah
    Hempstead and Mitchell Sinoway, a sin*apz Production.

5   Images of all of the works in the exhibition, reviews, installation
    photography, and the installation video can be viewed on the
    exhibition Web page at *www.lalouver.com/html/hockney_07.html.*

6   *David Hockney: The East Yorkshire Landscape,* Tate Britain,
    London, England, 11 June 2007 – 3 February 2008.

7   *Hockney on Turner Watercolors,* Tate Britain,
    London, England, 11 June 2007 – 3 February 2008.

8   *A Closer Winter Tunnel, February – March, 2006,*
    oil on six canvases, each panel: 36 x 48 in. (91.5 x 381 cm) /
    overall: 75 x 150 in. (190.5 x 381 cm),
    reproduced in *David Hockney: A Year in Yorkshire,*
    published by Annely Juda Fine Art, London, 2006.

9   *Nymphéas by Claude Monet,* Musée de l'Orangerie,
    Paris, France, reopened in May 2006.

10 *Summer Exhibition 2007,* Royal Academy of Arts,
    London, England, 11 June – 19 August 2007.

An early announcement for this ambitious 50-canvas
painting was distributed by Hockney's studio
to friends and colleagues:

Coming Up at the Royal Academy
A BIGGER SENSATION:
A Handmade Oil Painting
Recently done "en plein air" by D. Hockney, R.A.
Bigger Trees Near Warter or/ou "Peinture Sur Le Motif
Pout Le Nouvel Age Post-Photographique"

— David Hockney, March 2007

11 Martin Gayford, "A Bigger Picture,"
    Royal Academy Magazine, Summer 2007, pp. 48-51.

12 *David Hockney: Retrospektive Photoworks,*
    Museum Ludwig, Cologne, Germany, 1997.

13 *David Hockney: Exciting Times Are Ahead,*
    Kunst und Ausstellungshalle der Bundesrepublik
    Deutschland, Bonn, Germany, 2001.

14 *David Hockney: Espace/Paysage,*
    Centre Pompidou, Paris, France, 1999.

15 *Looking at Landscape | Being in Landscape,*
    L.A. Louver, Venice, California,
    15 September – 24 October 1998.

16 David Hockney, *Secret Knowledge:*
    Rediscovering the Lost Techniques
    of the Old Masters; first published in 2001 -
    by Thames & Hudson, London; the new
    and expanded edition published in 2006.

For additional reference, please see the exhibition
catalogue for *Velázquez,* The National Gallery,
London, England, 18 October 2006 – 21 January 2007.

WHY GO ON PAINTING IN YORKSHIRE?

Is it possible to do anything new in the landscape genre?
Most of the art world thinks it's not worth doing anymore.

In Europe, the idea grew that painting was finished, not needed.
This is because it had been replaced by something —
the photograph — the pencil of nature, the truth itself.

This assumes photography is modern; at least it's only
180 years old. If one rejects the "immaculate conception"
theory of photography — it came from nowhere,
about 1839 — one begins to see another history.

The optical projective of nature is a view of the world
from one point. It is not a human view.
The camera sees surfaces, we see space.

If one begins to see that both perspective (one point) and chiaroscuro
come, not from observing nature, as art history suggests, but from
observing the optical projection of it on a flat surface, as I suggest,
one gets a very different view of the past and of today. (Is film stuck
because it just uses one camera to make pictures and is therefore
Alberti's window, which now seems to be a prison?)

It is the position I now find myself in, realising that two hundred years ago
Constable would have thought the optical projection of nature was something
to aim for. I now know it is not — so stand in the landscape you love,
try and depict your feelings of space, and forget photographic vision,
which is distancing us too much from the physical world.

David Hockney
February 2007

Woldgate Woods, March 30 – April 21 2006
oil on six canvases
overall: 73 x 146" (185.4 x 370.8 cm)

Woldgate Woods III, May 20 & 21 2006
oil on six canvases
overall: 73 x 146" (185.4 x 370.8 cm)

Woldgate Woods, 26, 27 & 30 July 2006 2006
oil on six canvases
overall: 73 x 146" (185.4 x 370.8 cm)

Woldgate Woods, 6 & 9 November 2006 2006
oil on six canvases
overall: 73 x 146" (185.4 x 370.8 cm)

Woldgate Woods, 7 & 8 November 2006 2006
oil on six canvases
overall: 73 x 146" (185.4 x 370.8 cm)

Woldgate Woods, 26, 27 & 30 July 2006 2006
oil on six canvases
overall: 73 x 146" (185.4 x 370.8 cm)

Woldgate Woods, 6 & 9 November 2006 2006
oil on six canvases
overall: 73 x 146" (185.4 x 370.8 cm)

Woldgate Woods, 7 & 8 November 2006 2006
oil on six canvases
overall: 73 x 146" (185.4 x 370.8 cm)

Woldgate Woods, March 30 – April 21 2006
oil on six canvases
overall: 73 x 146" (185.4 x 370.8 cm)

overleaf: **Woldgate Woods III, May 20 & 21** 2006
oil on six canvases
overall: 73 x 146" (185.4 x 370.8 cm)

Woldgate Woods, 26, 27 & 30 July 2006 2006
oil on six canvases
overall: 73 x 146" (185.4 x 370.8 cm)

previous page:

Woldgate Woods, 7 & 8 November 2006 2006
oil on six canvases
overall: 73 x 146" (185.4 x 370.8 cm)

Woldgate Woods III, May 20 & 21 2006
oil on six canvases
overall: 73 x 146" (185.4 x 370.8 cm)

Woldgate Woods, March 30 – April 21 2006
oil on six canvases
overall: 73 x 146" (185.4 x 370.8 cm)

Woldgate Woods, 26, 27 & 30 July 2006 2006
oil on six canvases
overall: 73 x 146" (185.4 x 370.8 cm)

this page:

Steep Valley, Kirkby Underdale 2006
oil on two canvases
overall: 48 x 72" overall (121.9 x 182.9 cm)

Wheat Field Beyond the Tunnel, 16 August 2006 2006
oil on canvas
36 x 48" (91.4 x 121.9 cm)

Warter Vista 2006
oil on two canvases
overall: 48 x 72" overall (121.9 x 182.9 cm)

Tree Off The Track 2006
oil on four canvases
overall: 72 x 96" overall (182.9 x 243.8 cm)

Barley, Wheatfield + Borridge Ruston Parva 2006
oil on two canvases
overall: 48 x 72" overall (121.9 x 182.9 cm)

Elderflower Blossom, Kilham, July 2006
oil on two canvases
overall: 48 x 72" overall (121.9 x 182.9 cm)

Walnut Trees 2006
oil on canvas
36 x 48" (91.4 x 121.9 cm)

Woldgate Winter Tree 2006
oil on canvas
36 x 48" (91.4 x 121.9 cm)

Looking East 2006
oil on canvas
36 x 48" (91.4 x 121.9 cm)

Woldgate Winter Tree 2006
oil on canvas
36 x 48" (91.4 x 121.9 cm)

Walnut Trees 2006
oil on canvas
36 x 48" (91.4 x 121.9 cm)

Tree Off The Track 2006
oil on four canvases
overall: 72 x 96" overall (182.9 x 243.8 cm)

Elderflower Blossom, Kilham, July 2006
oil on two canvases
overall: 48 x 72" overall (121.9 x 182.9 cm)

Warter Vista 2006
oil on two canvases
overall: 48 x 72" overall (121.9 x 182.9 cm)

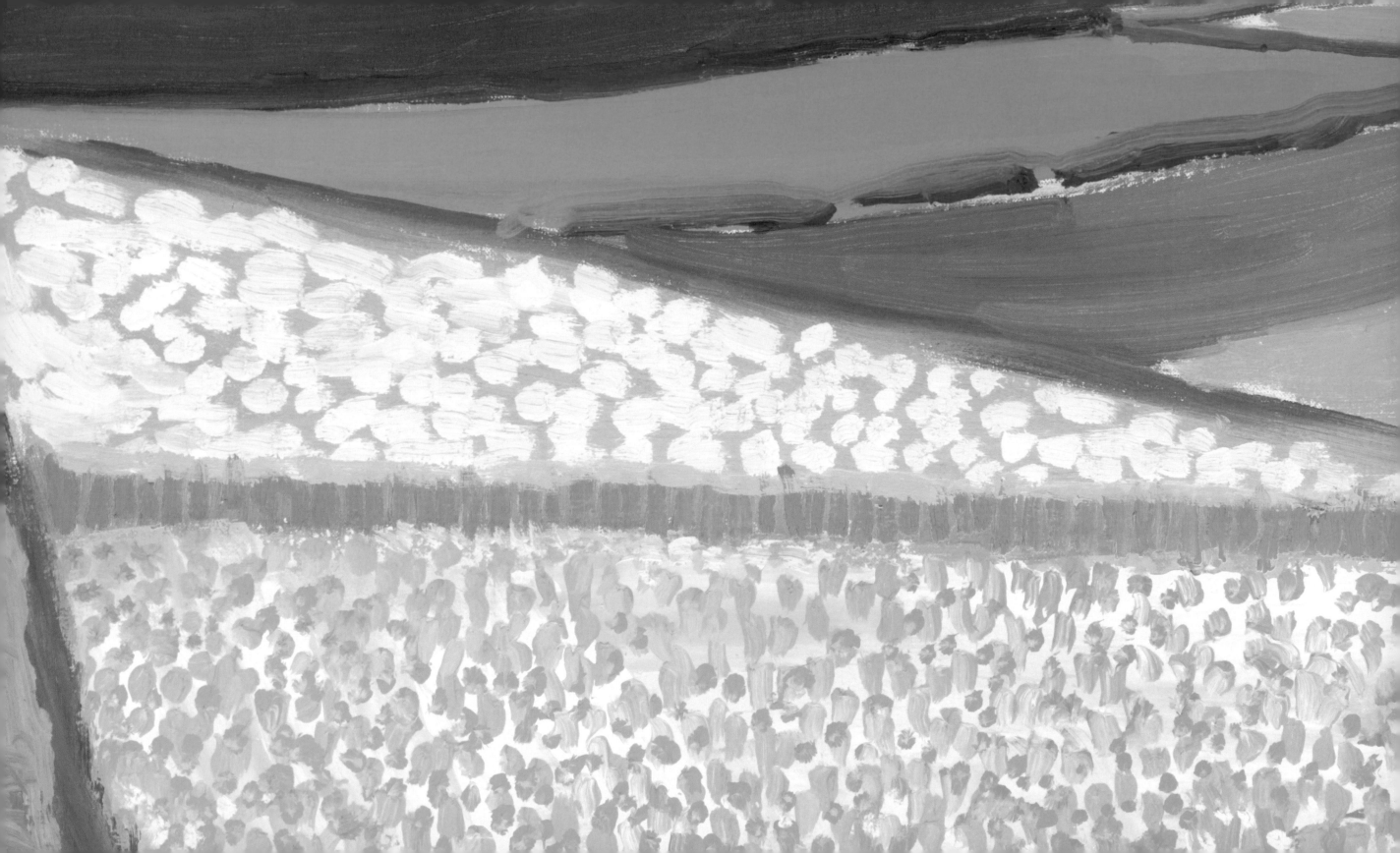

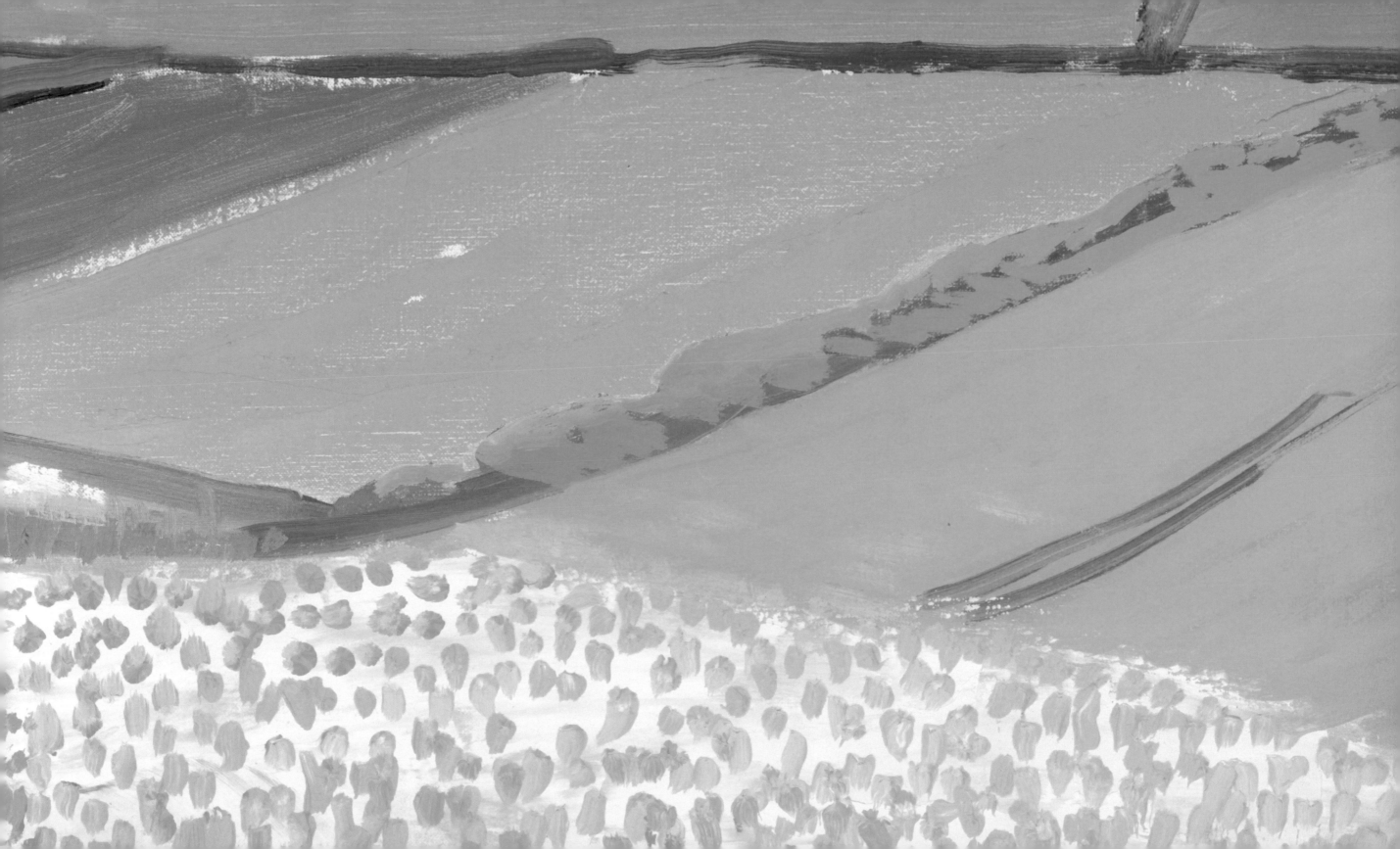

Barley, Wheatfield + Borridge Ruston Parva 2006
oil on two canvases
overall: 48 x 72" overall (121.9 x 182.9 cm)

Harvesting Near The Road to Thwing 2006
oil on canvas
36 x 48" (91.4 x 121.9 cm)

Steep Valley, Kirkby Underdale 2006
oil on two canvases
overall: 48 x 72" overall (121.9 x 182.9 cm)

Wheat Field Beyond the Tunnel, 16 August 2006 2006
oil on canvas
36 x 48" (91.4 x 121.9 cm)

David Hockney
The East Yorkshire Landscape

Credits

L.A. LOUVER

Peter Goulds
Kimberly Davis
Elizabeth East
Lisa Jann
Christopher Pate
Ted Conrad
Dana Gildenhorn
Dan Manns
Melissa Tolar
Alice Flather
Lindsey Christensen

DAVID HOCKNEY STUDIO

Gregory Evans
Jean-Pierre Goncalves
Karen Kuhlman
Richard Schmidt
Julie Pavlowski
Greg Rose
David Graves

L.A. Louver
45 North Venice Boulevard
Venice, California 90291
Tel 310 822 4955
Fax 310 821 7529
www.lalouver.com

Library of Congress Control Number:
2006940987
ISBN 0-1234567-8-9

East Yorkshire documentary photography:
Jean-Pierre Goncalves © David Hockney

Paintings and exhibition installation photography:
Richard Schmidt © David Hockney

David Hockney Studio
www.hockneypictures.com

Digital color management:
Erik Arnesen for Aegir Productions, Inc.
and **Richard Schmidt**

Catalogue coordination by Lisa Jann
for L.A. Louver

Design by Stefan G. Bucher
for 344design.com

Printing by Typecraft Wood & Jones
Pasadena, California

Printed on paper containing a minimum
of 10% post-consumer recovered fiber